POETRY ORIGINALS

Strange Goings-on

Other Poetry Originals

SERIES EDITOR: ANNE HARVEY

POETRY ORIGINALS

by Diana Hendry

Strange Goings-on

Illustrated by
Valerie Littlewood

VIKING

For Molly Green and Benedict Edwards

VIKING

Published by the Penguin Group
Penguin Books Ltd, 27 Wrights Lane, London w8 5TZ, England
Penguin Books USA Inc., 375 Hudson Street, New York, New York 10014, USA
Penguin Books Australia Ltd, Ringwood, Victoria, Australia
Penguin Books Canada Ltd, 10 Alcorn Avenue, Toronto, Ontario, Canada M4V 3B2
Penguin Books (NZ) Ltd, 182–190 Wairau Road, Auckland 10, New Zealand

Penguin Books Ltd, Registered Offices: Harmondsworth, Middlesex, England

First published 1995
1 3 5 7 9 10 8 6 4 2

Text copyright © Diana Hendry, 1995
Illustrations copyright © Valerie Littlewood, 1995
Introduction copyright © Anne Harvey, 1995

Acknowledgements are due to the editors of the following journals and anthologies:
Ambit, *Poetry Matters*, the *Poetry Book Society Anthology Annual 3* and the *Spectator*.
'The Builder's House', 'All Hail the Hollyhocks', 'Dressing Mother', 'Great-
grandma and James Andrew', 'Christmas' copyright © Diana Hendry, 1995, from
Making Blue, 1995, reprinted by permission of Peterloo Poets.

Filmset in Linotron Bembo by
Rowland Phototypesetting Ltd, Bury St Edmunds, Suffolk

Made and printed in Great Britain by Butler & Tanner Ltd, Frome and London

A CIP catalogue record for this book is available from the British Library

ISBN 0–670–86219–3

Contents

Introduction

Recently I visited Diana Hendry in her attractive house on a hill in Bristol. The whole place is welcoming; the bright red front door leads to more colour and warmth inside. There are books everywhere, in solid wooden bookcases, as well as lining the stairway. There are many pictures: a portrait of an unknown lady over the sitting-room mantelpiece, a sampler made by a very young Diana for her mother, with the name Amelia painstakingly stitched. It hangs beside her mother's photograph, close to another of Diana herself with her two older sisters. In one room an apple mobile is suspended from the ceiling.

Diana Hendry and I discovered that our first experiences of poetry were similar. She grew up by the sea on the Wirral Peninsula and I was in London, but we both attended elocution lessons, where good speech was taught and countless poems had to be learnt by heart. Nowadays this might be thought old-fashioned, but we enjoyed it, and Diana found that learning a poem by heart . . . 'brought about an intimacy between me and the poem'. The certificates and medals collected for passing the examinations set by the Poetry Society were less rewarding than gaining an appreciation for the styles and moods of poetry. Anyway, we agreed, what were you meant to *do* with the medals?

Diana has always been very short-sighted, but large spectacles in no way hide her expressive face and eyes. As we talked I could easily picture her as a small girl declaiming in tragic tones Walt Whitman's 'O Captain! my Captain!' and relishing the rhythm of John Masefield's 'I must go down to the seas again'. She was affected by listening to her elocution teacher, Miss Armstrong, and the equally fine voices of the head teachers at her junior school, described in one of her poems:

'Miss Wilkins deep and low
Miss Clingoe high and sweet . . .'

'My memory is of a childhood spent listening in,' she told me. Voices, language and the sounds around her made lasting impressions: the unmistakable inflection of the doctor's 'Good-morning!'; her sister's friend whose voice had 'that kind of rough husk to it that trees might talk in – if trees could talk'; her middle sister singing 'You are my heart's delight!' There were other, indefinable sounds too: the house telling of its past; sea and seagulls; strange, musical names in the wireless weather forecast – Faroe, Stornaway . . .

Diana became a listener because, being by far the youngest, she was less listened to. In the third of her three 'sister' poems she explains:

'There wasn't much left
For the making of me . . .'

She kept many things to herself . . . poetry for one: that was precious, and a secret. She loved a borrowed copy of A.A. Milne's *When We Were Very Young* so much that she 'forgot' to return it, and somehow managed to 'hang on to' two other coveted anthologies as well. While not suggesting you follow her example, perhaps after so long she may be forgiven. One of these, *Modern Poetry*, which she thought 'the prettiest book ever, small, square, dark blue, with a drawing of the poet Rupert Brooke holding a rose at the beginning' had poets in it who seemed to talk to her. Yeats,

Hardy, Graves, and Brooke himself, became part of the poetry secret.

Diana's family were not bookish. A set of Dickens' novels, bound in blue and gold, were arranged for show in the bookcase, part of the furnishings. She had to keep her own books tidily in a cupboard. She was an avid reader, devouring everything from the Bible to Enid Blyton, borrowed from four different libraries, one of them part of Boots the chemist. Next to reading were the true family tales her mother told her when the other girls were at work and school. Diana and I have in common Russian–Jewish ancestors and she loved hearing of her Yiddisher grand-mother who spoke no English and wore a wig. In her poem 'Speaking Properly' she writes movingly of her, imagining her homesick for Russia and wondering:

'. . . what had she to say
to me, born continents away, born yesterday?'

Diana also listened to her mother's friend, Ida, tell stories of her past and to her father's well-rounded talk filled with effective pauses that held the attention marvellously. She was proud of the song he had published in 1926, 'I'll Be Your Daddy Now, Dear', and has a copy still.

After junior school there was no more poetry until, when she was about twenty, at the time of the Beatles and the Liverpool Poets in the 1960s, she rediscovered it. It was a book of Roger McGough's that fired her imagination all over again, and soon she began writing her own poetry. Of course she did not become a well-known writer overnight. There were years of hard work. While writing and experi-menting with stories and poems, she worked as a typist, a secretary in the literary department of the *Sunday Times*, a receptionist and a journalist on the *Western Mail*. She once got the sack for reading during office hours. Later, as a mature student, she took an English degree at Bristol University and is now a tutor there on the Creative Writing course.

Her numerous publications include picture books and novels for older children, among them *Double Vision* which reveals something of herself as a schoolgirl, and in which characters and events overlap into poems like 'The Clarks' House' and 'Guardian Angel'. In 1991 her very imaginative novel *Harvey Angell* won a Whitbread Award. In this the hollyhocks so vividly described 'jiggling about as if someone had tickled them' almost re-appear in her poem 'All Hail the Hollyhocks':

'. . . humming sun and sky
beyond everything
shaking with laughter . . . '

Diana's range of subjects is exciting. Surely no other poet has explored the spare room, or that magical invention that once whizzed on overhead tracks across department stores, carrying customers' money and returning the change. In some poems friends and family appear, among them her own grown-up children, Kate and Hamish. She told me, 'Poems often come in threes', and added, 'If one poem is very difficult, really hard work, the next is likely to slip out quite effortlessly.' For me, as a reader and editor, a good poem can illuminate, surprise, even shock, so I was intrigued to hear Diana say: 'You know a poem can tell the poet something completely unexpected too.'

In 1993 Diana spent six months in Crete, a time of space and change, a time that inspired a novel, *The Awesome Bird*, a diary of her visit, and more poetry. Her first adult collection *Making Blue* is also published this year.

Diana Hendry, as a child, had ambitions to sing like Frank Sinatra, or to be a concert pianist. Although she still plays the piano, I'm glad she became a writer, and one with an individual voice, an ear for the sound of language, an eye for the quirky and off-centre as well as the familiar, and an utterly original approach.

Anne Harvey, 1995

Playing House

They came like robins
and painted the outside of the house
a bright, careless blue.
They put pots of geraniums on the sill,
made a makeshift curtain out of a bedspread.
They had a dog on a string
and an old car always under repair.
The girl was scruffy and smiling
when she Sellotaped the notice on the door
saying, 'This is our house.'

It wasn't of course, not legally.
An old lady lived there
until she and the house
disintegrated together.
Towards the end of her life,
when her legs were wadded in grubby
bandages, she pushed an old pink push-chair
full of kindling, up and down the street each
day.
No relatives ever came.
I think she'd have liked the girl
and the gaudy blue paint
and the geraniums.

But now each window of the house
is blanked out
with the chipboard letter of the law
and there's a padlock on the door
and the geraniums, the girl and the dog are
                                    gone.

The old woman's in a box of wood
and the girl in one of cardboard.

Observation Post

The police want to use my house
as an observation post. Something
mysterious is going on, they say,
in the street behind mine. And they're right.
My Californian lilac's gone wild trying
to escape over the wall. All Sunday
the Jamaican couple quarrel in bird-song.
An unseen drummer drums his midnight blues
away and some nights there's a taxi
that hurts and hurts and hurts
waiting for someone who never comes.
Up high a happily married couple
of TV aerials sit side by side
in their chimneypots watching the stars.
There are tiles uncannily slipping
off roofs; curtains drawn all the time
at fifty-nine – such strange goings-on
in the street behind mine.

Nobody's Room

You have to make do
with the room you are given –
inherited, usually
from sister or brother.
It is not what you'd choose
and there's little to change –
your clothes in the cupboard,
the bed rearranged.

Though you close tight the window
each night you'll inhale
the flairs and the flaws
of the one here before
so that when you both wake
there'll be that in your eye
that isn't quite you
and isn't quite 'I'.

'This is *my* room,' you'll say
and fling wide the door,
'*my* dressing-gown is hanging here
and that's a sign for sure.
These are *my* books on the shelf
and in the mirror is myself –
so I'd be glad if you'd ignore
all those others, here before.'

Next Door

There are no animals in our house,
But next door – there's a place!
Cats that sing,
One cow with midge,
A hairy Something
That sits on the fridge.
On Monday they stroll
Their giraffe in the hall.

We have proper meals in our house,
But next door – there's a place!
Chips in bags,
Doughnuts in jam,
Noodles and mash,
Curry and Spam,
Every Tuesday
It's popcorn-and-stew day.

It's bedtime at nine in our house,
But next door – there's a place!
TV horrors,
All-night bops,
No homework tomorrow,
Late lollipops.
On Wednesday they sleep
On their still-bopping feet.

We wear proper clothes in our house,
But next door – there's a place!
Lots of badges,
Weird tattoos,
Hats like hedges,
A brooch of screws.
On Thursdays they're dressed
In purple-striped vests.

There's no dirt or dust in our house,
But next door – there's a place!
Gunge in the bath,
Slime in the sink,
Bugs in the bed,
Dregs in the drink.
They sometimes tidy
Their cobwebs on Friday.

We have furniture in our house,
But next door – there's a place!
Hammocks and fiddles,
Beanbags and boxes,
Sofas of cuddles,
Lots of old sockses.
Their Saturday fling
Is a stairway of string.

Somebody's come to our house.
Somebody knocks on the door.
Says, 'It's only me,
Can I stay for tea?
And perhaps for evermore?'
Somebody sits on our Sunday floor,
Somebody says, 'With a place like this,
Who'd want to live next door?'

Next-door's Cat

has a lonely look,
he can't keep up with change,
first divorce, then lodgers –
nothing seems the same.

There's a lot of coming and going,
and no one with regular hours,
he curls himself up for comfort,
he's lost his confident prowl.

His basket's in the hallway,
and when they're all away,
someone comes in to feed him
but he's forgotten how to play.

Not knowing who he belongs to
gives a sad droop to his tail,
he used to be part of something
that now he can't even name.

It was something to do with family,
it was more than a cosy bed,
it was being welcomed and wanted,
not just watered, flea-collared and fed.

Next-door's cat has a lonely look,
home just isn't quite home,
and though there are people in the house
he's a cat who lives alone.

The Clarks' House

Her house had an old granny in it,
very shrivelled and cross and essential
and a baby-sister in a de luxe pram.
Her father commanded the SS *Apollon*.
Her mother, plump as a robin, perched on
                                    stilettos,
commanded her very own cocktail bar.

They were all, apart from the baby,
wicked and vulgar
and didn't look after the garden
and had a shrunken head on the mantel.
It was their sign to the world
that the Clarks were untamed.

The Builder's House

This was Mills the builder's house:
outhouse after outhouse
at the back as if from the start
he was travelling out. The kitchen,
a shack at the side, had a stove and cold tap,
there were buckets to catch the leaks
from the roof, walls unpainted, rooms
unheated – the whole place neglected.

A lifetime he spent doing the houses
of others, his own left undone
but for one refinement – in every
dark cupboard he fixed a light.
And maybe he had his priorities right –
leaving the front of his life unpainted
and all the dark places light.

The Teapot's Lament

I'm a little teapot
quite upset,
my true-pot self
never met.

Thought you'd guess
by my flowery dress,
thought you'd know
by my bobble's glow,
thought if I posed
with hand on hip,
the other outstretched
as for a kiss,
you couldn't resist,
you wouldn't miss,
you'd see through the tannin
to who I am in
my shelf and self dreams
when late at night
I dance the polka
by candle-light
and up the kitchen
cakewalk and shimmy,
without a drop of water in me,
and rumba, samba,
two-step, tango,

cha-cha, Charleston and fandango,
Lambeth Walk and palais glide
and *paso doble* side to side.
Take me in your arms and waltz –
I'm a teapot with fond hopes.
Oh, I see it!
You just want tea!
You're not the true-heart
meant for me.

I'm a little teapot
in a huff,
not given the chance
to strut my stuff.

The Spare Room

It was just the spare room
the nobody-there room
the spooks-in-the-air room
the unbearable spare room.

It wasn't the guest room
the four-poster best room
the designed-to-impress room
the unusable guest room.

It wasn't the main room
the homely and plain room
the flop-on-the-bed room
Mum and Dad's own room.

It wasn't the blue room
the sweet lulla-loo room
the creep-on-your-feet room
the baby's asleep room.

It wasn't the bright room
the clothes-everywhere room
the music-all-night room
sister's scattered-about room.

It was just the spare room
the nobody-there room
the spooks-in-the-air room
the unbearable spare room.

Home

No one will come for us here. It is all
so cosy. See the fire twinkling
in the rustic grate? See the nursery's bars?
Our pillows are plump with ducky feathers;
the bolts on the door, snugly secure.
And then there's the moon-cloaked lady and
the waxwork dummy reading the paper –

they're such a nice couple. Ether impregnates
our curtains of velvet. The carpet hushes
each word as it falls. Sleep, being risky,
I rub my cheek on the sofa's rough stubble.
There's all the stairs of dark to go.
In the bay window, the piano raises
its wing like Tristram's black sail.* Outside

the siren that calls out the lifeboat wails out
what's in us. 'Distress,' the sea hisses,
swishing its skirts through our cabined dreams.

* The black sail is an omen in the legend of Tristram and
Iseult.

Stage Directions for Bluebells

OK. Everyone else off-stage –
we'll just have bluebells for this one.
Lilac? Don't fire your torches yet.
Daisies? Just stay folded, will you?
Now. Bluebells. Can we all be up-
standing? That's it! Spread yourselves
about a bit. Use the whole stage.
What d'you think we've got all this green
foliage for? Nice! Nice! Now families –
over on the right, please. And you two –
could you appear to be in conversation,
or at least on nodding acquaintance? No,
there's no need to be facetious. You don't
have to ring. Solitaries? Nestle in the shade
among the ferns and ivies. No, you can't
have extra lighting. It's contrast we're after.
OK. You shy, flirty ones – over by the wall.
Peep through the peonies. Can you tremble?
Very nice! Miss Precocious? By the rose.
Now. You extras. All right, all righty,
individuals. We're running out of space here.
Do what you can with the cracks in the path.
Yes, I realize you might get trampled on –
that's just a risk you've got to take.

Lovely! Lovely! You all look very picturesque.
OK. That's it! Hold it! Hold it!
We'll call it 'Late April in England, with
                                    bluebells'.

Apple Sense

To live with an apple tree
in your garden is not
to understand it. Today,
for example, it stands
on one leg, answers
February's ice with a snarl
of black spikes. In summer
its leaves are tarnished,
its fruit beyond reach.
There's an exchange going on
between light, weather,
time and tree in which I'm
a bystander, asker
of inane questions
in the wrong language.

The tree's rhythm, for
example – bough's rise
and fall – was it learnt
from the sea? Does it mind
that what was orchard
is now city street? Has it
Eden in its genes? Who
is it here for? Balance
and symmetry – imposed or
chosen – seem what it's about,
though the more I look
the less I know. It's
as though some extra sense,
an apple sense, were needed,
a cure for sight's blindness,
an ear for sap, a way
of speaking in blossom.

Apple and Lilac

My apple tree's put its glad rags on –
pink and green
pink and green
Its flowers are silky as ice-cream –
pink and green
pink and green

The lilac holds its torches high –
it's most impressed
most impressed
to see my apple, blossom-blessed.

All Hail the Hollyhocks

Freaks, flapping their leaves
like albatross wings when
to be discreet they should lean
against some husbanding wall,
pose prettily beside a door.

Exposed and unsupported
these show-offs flaunt their flowers
in public. Neat, low clumps
of things mumble at their feet,
the clingers and grippers,
the rooters and spreaders,
who talk of decorum.

The hussies ignore them, intent
on the terrible toil of growing,
the doubtful strength,
the engorged bud,
the threat of snail slime, rust and slug,
and the shame
of being too tall, too much,
too altogether hollyhock.

Well, now they're wind instruments
flowering at every stop.
They're summer's gothic,
they're hitting the high spots,
they're shooting their mouths off
hysterical to have made it
past the clothes-line
past the first-floor windows.

Gangling, tranced teenagers with earphones on,
they're humming sun and sky,
beyond everything,
shaking with laughter.
Tomorrow they'll flash another flower or two

they're going straight through.

Bulbs

Like an addict in need of supplies, I buy bags
and bags of them. They nuzzle each other
inside the brown paper. I've a lust for them
like a pregnant woman for a certain food.

I set them out on the kitchen table. The raw
light hurts them. They want to be snugged
in the moist, dark bed. The root
of this daffodil is like several dead spiders.

This crocus is postmarked with a small brown
sun. They wear threadbare vests of pencil-
shavings, darned with dark soil from their past
earth lives. Some have a small white fang

at the tip. I don't want to plant them. I'd
like to leave them, as candles keeping vigil
in the night; hold one in my hand all winter,
forgo spring's gaudy show of gold and keep

these rough and awkward hope-packed things.

Father and Son

Grandad was a rebel –
wouldn't work, wouldn't save,
lived off his son, had fun,
wouldn't behave,
married again at seventy-seven,
a platinum blonde all curls and beads.
Told by my dad to act his age
Grandad just laughed up his borrowed sleeve,
did as he pleased.

Dad worked hard, saved,
kept us in shoes, stayed
with my mother,
stuck with the rules, never
had time to play the fool
and when he died, awfully early,
left us his money, his house, and his pearly

cuff-links to Grandad, who lived on and on
but had to work hard at having fun,

missing the son he'd leant upon.

Dressing Mother

I help roll her stockings over her feet,
then up to her knees. She's managed her dress
but I free her fingers from the sleeves.
Before the mirror she rouges her cheeks,
combs her thin curls, hands me a bow.
It's scarlet and goes on a ribbon I thread
under her collar and fix with a hook.
Over an hour to dress her today.

Such an innocence stays at the nape of the neck
it fumbles my fingers. I see her binding
bands of scarlet at the ends of my plaits
and fastening the buttons at my back.
Now look – she's dressed as a child off
to some party. I straighten her scarlet bow

and don't want her to go,
don't want her to go.

A Greeting Card

For Molly Green

Baby, they are building new rooms for you.
A washing machine has been ordered,
grandmas are in waiting,
one of your sisters is practising
for your arrival
by bathing her family of trolls
then dusting their tums with talc.
(The trolls have orange, green and purple hair.)

Cots and prams are being assessed,
names tried out.
All over the country women are knitting.
On the family circuit
there's a buzz of excitement
as news of you goes on the air.
It's as if we are all preparing
new rooms in our hearts
by way of saying

you're welcome,
you're welcome,
you're welcome.

See My Daughter?

For Kate

See her curls? See her smile?
See how good you feel when she walks by?
See how the trees nod to her and bow?
See how much friendlier the room is when she's
                                                in it?
See how when she comes out, the sun comes
                                            with her?
See how the seagulls hurry inland to search her
                                                out?
See how spring sets his watch by her pulse?
See how the greengrocer's apples grow glossier
                                        just looking?
See how the buskers brighten their flutes?
See how the hollyhocks laugh?
See how the moon melts?
See how the stars change to thousand–watt
                                            bulbs?
See how when she came into the world
        the whole world grew brighter?

See my daughter?

Kate Bathing

In the prow of the bath,
pigtails – a laurel wreath –
pinned up on her head.
Her shoulders open
like butterfly wings.
With a dripping sponge
she lacquers her cheeks.
A patch of back's
as out of reach
as self.

You wonder in what timeless
stream she dipped her eyes
to make them shine so clear.

Great-grandma and James Andrew

It's not me they want in the photograph –
it's history they're after.
I'll not be part of it.
They can sit me on the sofa
and put the baby on my lap
and measure out, in black and white,
almost a century's gap
between me – great-grandma – eighty-four –
and James Andrew, newly born.

I can't refuse the pose. I can't refuse
the years. I can't refuse the law –
new life for old. But I won't smile.
I'll hold the baby, fold my hands
so he doesn't fall. When I stare
at the camera as I'm bid, I don't see
the birdie any more. Only the dark.

James Andrew turns his head aside.
The light from the garden has caught his eye.
He hasn't learnt to pose and lie.
His fingers tickle. That child will be
the death of me.

A Letter to My Son

For Hamish

After twenty-five years
you're still a surprise –
the flatness of you,
the straightness of leg,
the mystery
of what goes on
in your head and how
you've outgrown me. Some-
times I think a nettle
might feel as odd
sprouting a rose
or a hedgehog a hawk
as I, growing a son.

You're one of *them*,
the incomprehen-
sible Other, and yet
as familiar to me
as the nose on my face.

I watch how quietly
you shoulder your sorrows,
not going on
and on about life –
as your sister might –
not having, it seems,

that female compulsion
to clean out the house.

I watch you out
in the world's rough weather,
I watch the girls
and huff my feathers
at those who fail
to see you're the flower
of the flock, the title-
holder, the beau ideal.

How curious
this love of mine
for you. Almost
I could map out
its boundary lines
far and near,
close and apart,
and give an address:

Main Stream,
Centre,
Heart.

Big Sister

For Leila

Like Boadicea
she rode into town
in the prow of the bus –
our pioneer
to that fantasy land
of Being-Grown-Up.

Stage-door fans
to her Hollywood star,
we eavesdropped the rhythm
of her Singer's treadle
as she pedalled enchantments
of sequins and satins,
her mouth full of pins,
her head full of patterns.

We spied on the secrets
of her magic den –
blushers and shadows
juice of flowers
sticks of scarlet
black mascaras
bangles, charms.

Lurking on landings,
crouched behind sofas,
on a Richter Scale
of romance and longing
we rated the princes,
and found them all wanting.

Acned and anxious
we waited our turn,
keen to inherit
her route-maps, her cast-offs,
her place in Their hearts,
expecting her always
to come to our rescue,
take the sting from our hurts

and be our brave front
because she was the first.

The Middle One

For Julie

She was the one
they sent away.
Each new term's start
turned the world grey.

In the big double bed
alone I slept,
and how empty her place
beside me felt.

She was the one
who struggled for answers,
she was the one
left out of romances.

She was the one
who made me cocoa,
sang *Gilbert and Sullivan*
in a sweet soprano.

She was the one
betwixt and between,
the family baby
and the first-born queen.

She was the one
whose label hurt,
she was the one
who chose to desert.

She was the one
who proved them wrong,
jumping out of the middle,
to sing her own song.

The Youngest

I'm the smallest
of the three,
there wasn't much left
for the making of me

so they had to use scraps
and bits and pieces,
eyes from a great-aunt,
nose of the nieces.

I'm the smallest
of the three,
a hotch-potch, patchwork
made-up me.

David

I should have been David,
the son they so wanted,
they had his name ready,
they had the blue gear
and two older sisters
to look after him here.
But fate double-crossed them
and I came along –
as his little impostor
I knew I was wrong.

If, as I think,
the unborn have ghosts,
then David's the one
who haunts me most.
He borrows my thoughts,
he calls me a phoney,
says that it's he
should be here,
he'd come into his own
if I'd just disappear.

But over the years
we've come to agree
that I'm as much David
as David is me.
He the dream child,
I the one born,
but sharing together
that gossamer space,
where dream and reality
meet and join.

Mrs Rice

When my mother went away
Mrs Rice came to stay.
Mrs Rice was plain as rice,
as good as rice,
as dull as rice.
She walked so quietly up the stair,
I thought that there was no one there.
She didn't beat me up or shout,
she hadn't any secret vice,
she said her prayers, I have no doubt
that Mrs Rice was very nice.

When Mrs Rice came to stay
the bright geraniums faded away,
the furniture shrank,
the house turned chill,
the light on the landing
looked pale and ill.
And Mrs Rice lingered there,
doing what was expected of her.

How glad I was when my mother returned
and the geraniums fired
and the furniture bloomed
and the laughter burned.
My mother's laugh was loud and gay
and Mrs Rice was sent away.

A Little Night Knitting for Nain

For Kezia Kernighan

Always together
but often apart
dust your knuckles
warm your heart
hold you close
but leave you free
to twiddle your thumbs
or climb a tree.
Soft as kittens
what can they be?
The fingerless mittens
Nain knitted for me.

First Love

They say I should not wait about your street,
nor call upon your friends to hear of you,
or go to places where by chance we'll meet
or hold your hand unless you ask me to.
They tell me I should emphasize my waist
and cultivate the arts that make men thirst:
should learn to waken lust and yet stay chaste
and I should never say 'I love you' first.

But I would come to you clear-eyed and plain,
my treasures in a kerchief wrapped. To you
I'd give the first primrose, a daisy chain,
a lucky stone, my heart for your tattoo.
And when, in time, they say, 'We told you so',
my truth I'll have and they their status quo.

The Catch

My sister said it was time
I went out in the world
and she would take me
so I kissed my parents goodbye
(they looked ashamed) and I
went out in the world
on no particular night
and returned on Thursday.

I went in the clothes I stood in
to the Presbyterian Youth Club Hall
and knew them all
and recognized no one
until the boy –
like an otter from under water –
with oiled black hair and a glossy blazer,
came to return my name.

And there I was
landed, and larger than I expected
and an odd shape
wearing a flared blue skirt and child's shoes
most uncomfortable
yet delighted.

First School

My two head teachers
had a tower each,
leaned out their windows,
talked across the breach –
Miss Wilkins deep and low,
Miss Clingoe high and sweet.

I never heard the words they spoke,
I only heard the tune;
Miss Wilkins with her deep-down bell,
Miss Clingoe on her flute –
the sounds went soaring in my head
and wriggled to my feet.

I didn't learn to read or write,
or add up two and two,
by rise and fall, by bell and flute,
by the music they made together,
I learnt about the human heart,
its reaches and its weathers.

Streams

When we went to the grammar school
the teacher said,
'You A-stream girls
will go out in the world
and be doctors and lawyers.
You C-stream girls
will go out in the world
and be typists and mothers.'

But when we left
(tossing our hats in the air),
beyond the school borders,
the streams overflowed
and the dams broke
with the water hoarded
in our hearts
and all the girls flowed
out in the world
in alphabetical disorder.

Easter in the Park

A skyful of kites
and the computer program
in my head flashes its files up from limbo
'bird'   'heart'   'spirit'   'flight'.
I try to cancel, I feel so corny,
but surprise has opened my mouth,
filched out my heart,
attached a string,
turned
   it
      downside
         up
         and
            set
             it
              in

               flight.

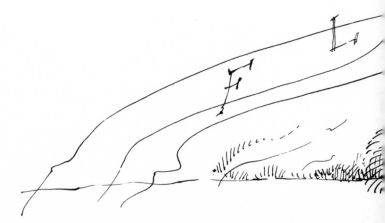

Speaking Properly

For Charles Tomlinson

There can be no going back now
to my Russian gran
snapped in the back yard one summer
shy and untidy and still in her apron
as if a moment was all could be taken
from cooking and cleaning and washing for ten.
My great-gran's down in the basement
hid in her orthodox wig and her Yiddish.

As a child I thought theirs the exodus
after Moses, saw them coming like Cossacks
on husky-pulled sledges in icicled furs.
They were my romantic ancestors
who mortified my mum with their foreign ways,
their Vees and their Vyes and their Vobble-yous,
the X on the nationalization papers
that listed the men and the children
but left out the wives. We turned

our backs on them, put up lace curtains
like the Berlin Wall, went off to the shires
to learn to speak nicely and only later
felt their loss. I'd think of great-gran
home-sick for Riga, and heart-sick myself
for a *mama-loshen*,★ try to raise her ghost
and ask a few questions. She'd haunt
but not answer. Now, writing her off,
I understand why. She who'd had words
with Moses – Ai-yi-yi! – what had she to say
to me, born continents away, born yesterday?

★*mama-loshen*: mother tongue

55

Elegy for a Much-loved Dog

How beautiful she was
With her amber eyes
Ears hemmed like silk purses
Their insides soft as the petals of iris
Her hound's high haunches
Her poor docked stump of a tail.

How afraid she was
Of the paper lampshade's ghostly shifting
Of the dragon fire of hot-air balloons
Of the vet's cold floor
Of being alone.

How comforting she was
With her welcoming skid down the stairs
Her grunts and snuffles in the creaky basket
Her jump and flump on the bed
The collapse of legs, the warm dump
Of herself, her dry biscuity smell,
Her contented 'Humph'.

How she could lift the heart
In exuberant take-off after a rabbit
How, for her, our going out
Into field or wood, was a going home.
How elegant her trot, her point,
Her pose on the seat in the window
How she was the book
Of the children's childhood.

How long her dying took.

Hallowe'en with Sue

For Sue Heap

Without a map, your flying slippers
arrive on my doorstep.
Bird men on stilts appear.
Books float on water. Cowboys
in the wide open spaces of Wyoming
reach, unforgiven, for their holsters.
The ghosts of steam trains whoop through
                              tunnels,

scarf cranes in smoke, turn
the sky to Turner. Twenty years late
Dr Who arrives. A man wearing
a bright yellow rubber glove
as a hat sets fire to his fingers.

It's Hallowe'en and we're off
to Mozartland. We're travelling
by Poem. The Lord only knows
where we're living
or where we're going.

Christmas

is never where you expect it.
Not in the big house
with the fire lit and the presents rustling,
nor when the lights awaken
the tree and you should feel something
and don't.
Christmas happens in an unimaginable
place – in a city store with canned music –
in the street with a stranger
and a white cyclamen,
or when the silence tightens
the cry in your throat.

Then Christmas comes,
never where you expect it
and always in Bethlehem.

The Guardian Angel

Well, I had my list
and He had His
and I thought, 'There's enough
on mine to get me in.'

But from His face
I could tell
He didn't think much
of awards and honours
and that kind of stuff –
even cheques to Oxfam
didn't earn me a plus.

Then His finger paused
at a single line
and He said with a smile,
'I see you played
guardian angel
to a frightened child.

'She lived in the house
across the street
and through your open curtains
saw your light –
it comforted her
night after night.'

'Bless me,' I said,
'but I don't remember.'
'I do,' said He.
'Come on in. Enter.'

Par Avion

More than prayers, planes and paper darts,
more than birds, boomerangs and buttresses,
more than fireworks, flags and fleas,
more than all the other things that fly,
I loved the shuttle in the shop. I'd watch
the shop-girl snuggle the money and the bill
inside then set it flying on its wire up
to the counting house in the sky of *Accounts*.

Down on earth I'd wait for the shuttle's return
hoping for something unexpected – a message
perhaps, a surprise flower or picture
of a smile – not the heart subtracted from hope
and then let down with a neatly done sum
and a few pennies change. By a space shuttle
of kinds, I send you this poem. It's in love
with impossibility, distance and no time at all.

Hope it smiles at you. Hope it's something
unexpected. Hope it flies on the wires
of kingdom come. Hope it rings all the tills
from here to there. Hope, when you hold it
it tugs at your heart like the string of a kite.
Hope it's light. Hope it will so take the imprint
of life that death will pale. Hope it spits
in the eye of time passing. Hope it's lasting.

Index of First Lines